Managing shift work

Health and safety guidance

HSE Books

First published 2006

ISBN 0 7176 6197 0

This guidance is issued by the Health and Safety Executive. Following the guidance is not compulsory and you are free to take other action. But if you do follow the guidance you will normally be doing enough to comply with the law. Health and safety inspectors seek to secure compliance with the law and may refer to this guidance as illustrating good practice.

Contents

Introduction

1 This guidance aims to improve safety and reduce ill health by:

- making employers aware of their duty under law to assess any risks associated with shift work;
- improving understanding of shift work and its impact on health and safety;
- providing advice on risk assessment, design of shift-work schedules and the shift-work environment;
- suggesting measures employers, safety representatives and employees can use to reduce the negative impact of shift work;
- reducing fatigue, poor performance, errors and accidents by enabling employers to control, manage and monitor the risks of shift work.

2 The guidance is aimed at employers, safety representatives, trade union officials, employees, regulators and other stakeholders.

Background

Duty under law

3 The Working Time Regulations 1998 (as amended) (WTR) lay down the minimum legal requirements on how to organise working time.[1,2] Some workers in certain sectors, such as the aviation industry and mobile workers in road and sea transport are currently exempt from WTR and are subject to specific legislation that relates to working time. The basic rights and protections that WTR provide are outlined in Appendix 1.

4 In addition to WTR, workers doing safety-critical work on the railways are also subject to the Railway and Other Guided Transport Systems (Safety) Regulations 2006. [3,4] These Regulations include a duty to make arrangements to prevent serious consequences arising from tired/fatigued employees and so endanger safety.

5 It is not however sufficient to rely on the above requirements to ensure that you meet your obligations for health and safety in regard to shift-working arrangements (see Appendix 1). When you organise and plan shift work, you must also comply with employers' general duties under the Health and Safety at Work etc Act 1974 (the HSW Act)[5] and the Management of Health and Safety at Work Regulations 1999 (MHSWR).[6] Under the HSW Act all employers, including the self employed, have a duty, so far as it is reasonably practicable, to protect the health, safety and welfare at work of all their employees. They also have a duty, so far as is reasonably practicable, to ensure that others are not exposed to health and safety risks through their undertaking.

6 Under MHSWR, employers are required to make an assessment of the risks to employees from work activities and make a commitment to introduce measures that are 'reasonably practicable' to remove or control these risks. This includes the number of hours worked and how these hours are scheduled.

7 Employees also have a duty to take reasonable care of their own health and safety and that of other people, who may be affected by their activities at work. This duty implies that employees should take positive steps to understand the risk factors in their work, such as the causes of fatigue, comply with safety rules and procedures and make sure that nothing they do or fail to do at work puts anyone at risk.

8 Under the Safety Representatives and Safety Committees Regulations 1977[7] and the Health and Safety (Consultation with Employees) Regulations 1996,[8,9] employers must consult with employees on health and safety matters. Consultation involves employers not only giving information to employees but also listening to and taking account of what employees say before they make any health and safety decisions. If a decision involving work equipment, processes or organisation could affect the health and safety of employees, such as any proposed changes to shift-working arrangements, the employer must allow time to give the employees (or their representatives) information about the proposals. The employer must also give the employees (or their representatives) the chance to express their views. Then the employer must take account of these views before reaching a decision.

What do we mean by shift work?

9 There is no specific definition of shift work in law, but it usually means:

- a work activity scheduled outside standard daytime hours, where there may be a handover of duty from one individual or work group to another;
- a pattern of work where one employee replaces another on the same job within a 24-hour period.[10,11]

10 Standard daytime hours are considered as:

- a work schedule involving an activity during the day, commonly for a period of eight hours between 7.00 am and 7.00 pm. There are usually two periods of work, one in the morning, the other in the afternoon, separated by a lunch-time break.

11 In this guidance, all systems of work other than standard daytime hours are considered as shift work. Examples of shift work might be:

- work during the afternoon, night or weekend, typically with periods of the work schedule outside standard daytime hours;
- extended work periods of 12 hours or more, often associated with compressing the working week;
- rotating hours of work;
- split shifts, where work periods are divided into two distinct parts with several hours break in between;
- overtime;
- standby/on-call duties.

Shift workers in the UK

12 The number of shift workers in the UK has gradually increased over the last 25 years reaching a peak in 2000, when around 15% of the working population (approximately 3.8 million people), worked shifts for 'most of the time'. Since then, numbers have stabilised, with around 14% of the working population (3.6 million people) now doing shift work 'most of the time'.[12]

13 In the past, shift work was traditionally associated with industries where 24-hour operation was either necessary (eg essential public services like hospitals, the police, the fire brigade and the utilities) or practical (eg the transportation, chemical, mining and other process and manufacturing industries). The recent upward trend in the percentage of people employed in shift work reflects an adoption of shift work beyond the traditional sectors.[11] For example supermarkets, petrol stations and call centres now commonly employ shift workers.

14 This trend has developed because of changes in society, supported by workers who are prepared to do shift work. There may be several reasons for this, such as the recent shift towards a 24-hour society, lack of employment options or a preference for compensatory factors such as flexible working, better pay or time off in lieu.

Assessing and managing the risks associated with shift work

15 The main principle of the HSW Act is that those who create risk from work activity are responsible for the protection of workers and the public from any consequences. As shift work may affect the health and safety of your employees and the public, it is important for you to control risks effectively and prevent harm to people.

16 The HSE publication, *Successful health and safety management*[13] describes a systematic approach to assessing and managing health and safety risks. An approach based on this, that you might wish to use to manage shift-working arrangements, is summarised in Figure 1.

17 This approach will allow you to assess and better organise your shift-work schedules. You may also wish to consult any specific guidance or standards of good practice that have been developed for your particular industry. Under certain circumstances, however, additional external expertise may be required, for example when:

- your organisation has difficulty making decisions;
- the planning and organisation of the shift-work schedule is too complex;
- there are safety critical issues to consider.

Sources of further information and help can be found in Appendix 4.

Consider the risks of shift work and the benefits of effective management.	■ What are the undesirable effects of shift work? ■ Consider the costs and benefits of effective management of shift-working arrangements.
Establish systems to manage the risks of shift work.	■ Seek management commitment to control the risks of shift work. ■ Identify individuals responsible for shift-working arrangements. ■ Involve safety representatives and workers.
Assess the risks associated with shift work in your workplace.	■ Consider the risks that workers may be exposed to. ■ Establish who might be harmed by shift work. ■ Consult workers and their safety representatives.
Take action to reduce these risks.	■ Assess how severe the risks are and identify where improvements need to be made. ■ Improve the shift-work schedule. ■ Improve the workplace environment. ■ Apply good practice guidelines.
Check and review your shift-work arrangements regularly.	■ Implement a system for early reporting of problems associated with shift work. ■ Monitor alterations to shift-work schedules and/or work conditions. ■ Periodically review the effectiveness of your shift-working arrangements.

Figure 1 A systematic approach to assessing and managing the risks associated with shift work

Consider the risks of shift work and the benefits of effective management

What are the undesirable effects of shift work?

18 Research has shown that there can be undesirable consequences for those working shifts outside standard daytime hours, particularly those covering the night or with early morning starts.[14,15] For example, shift work may result in:

- disruption of the internal body clock;
- fatigue;
- sleeping difficulties;
- disturbed appetite and digestion;
- reliance on sedatives and/or stimulants;
- social and domestic problems,

which in turn can affect performance, increase the likelihood of errors and accidents at work and might have a negative effect on health.

Disruption of the internal body clock (circadian rhythms)

19 By nature, humans are active and perform best during the day and need to sleep at night when performance is generally poorer. We follow this innate pattern because of an internal body clock, located in the brain which sets the daily cycle of biological activities, such as chemical and hormone release that influence body activity. For example, heart rate, blood pressure and body temperature are increased during the day. At night they are reduced and we slow down and feel sleepy. This daily cycle is known as the circadian rhythm and explains why we eat and sleep at similar times each day.[16] External factors or cues such as daylight, meal times, clocks and working hours help to regulate this internal body clock, and play an important role in keeping our bodies in step with the world around us.

20 Our internal body clock can change gradually, but for most people it is resistant to the abrupt changes in the sleep/wake cycle that are required by shift-work schedules or flying across time zones. This can cause our natural daily rhythms to become out of tune with those of the world around us. This is the reason why we can feel 'out of sorts' and less able to function to the best of our ability when we do not get enough sleep.

21 The adjustment of our internal body clock to an abrupt change in the sleep/wake cycle may take days or weeks. It will start to adjust body functions after a few days of shift work, but at different rates, so behaviours that rely on a regular cycle such as digestion, alertness and sleep are disturbed. The adjustment may be more successful in specialised work environments, such as submarines and oil rigs, where the effects of external cues are minimised. However, our internal body clock will never fully adjust, even for workers on permanent night shifts. Those regular night workers who change back to daytime routines during rest days will continue to suffer the consequences of a disrupted internal clock, as it attempts to reset to daylight rhythms during days off.

Sleep disturbance/loss

22 A consensus view by scientists who study human performance and safety is that sleep is a powerful and vital biological need. Insufficient and disturbed sleep, chronic sleep loss and being awake for prolonged periods, increases the risk of errors and accidents.[17,18]

23 Day sleep is usually lighter and shorter in duration and therefore less restorative than night sleep.[14] It is more often disturbed because of warmer temperatures and daytime activity such as the phone ringing, noisy children or domestic responsibilities. While we can rearrange some external cues, for example meal times, it is difficult to control all influential sleep/wake cues, particularly daylight. For example exposure to bright light at dawn after a night shift may make you less inclined to sleep.

24 People's adaptability means that we can, if we need to, resist our internal body clock and function for periods with either reduced sleep or even no sleep at all. The cost of resisting this need to sleep is known as a 'sleep debt'. The desire to recover this debt can be very hard to resist, particularly when external cues or our body's internal body clock are driving us to sleep.

25 Research reveals that when we are sleep deprived and/or fatigued, performance is affected and errors are more likely.[19,20] This particularly applies to tasks that require:

- vigilance and monitoring;
- decision making;
- awareness;
- fast reaction time;
- tracking ability;
- memory.

Fatigue

26 Fatigue is the decline in mental and/or physical performance that results from prolonged exertion, lack of quality sleep or disruption of the internal body clock.[21] The degree to which a worker is prone to fatigue is also related to workload. For example, work that requires constant attention, is machine paced, complex or monotonous will increase the risk of fatigue.[19]

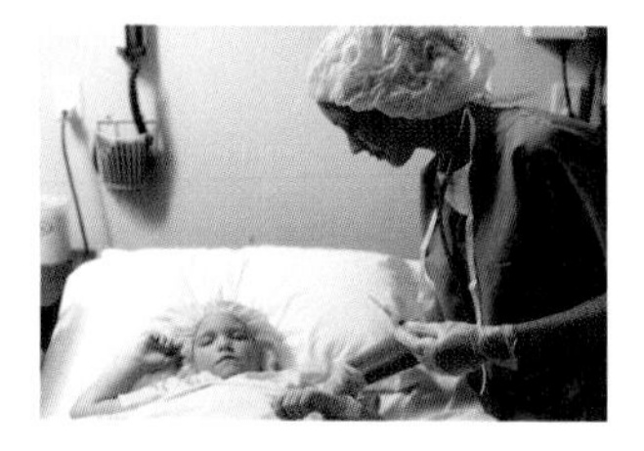

27 A poor balance between the demands of work and the time provided for rest and recovery, resulting for example, from poorly designed shift-work schedules and long working hours is likely to result in chronic fatigue.

28 Levels of fatigue are also affected by personal factors such as home life or individual characteristics. You will need to be aware of these factors when you carry out your risk assessment, but you are not expected to control them.

29 The consequences of fatigue include reduced alertness, poor and slow perception and sleepiness.[19] Chronic fatigue has also been associated with a number of long-term health problems.[21]

Errors, productivity and accidents

30 For shift working to be financially viable, you need to maintain a satisfactory level of productivity and safety. Fatigued shift workers may perform less well than those working standard daytime hours, especially during periods of low alertness. The consequences of this could range from relatively minor events to serious accidents. Take both ends of this spectrum into account when you are assessing the cost-effectiveness of shift working as the social and financial costs of frequent minor events may equate over time to those associated with a rarely occurring serious accident.

31 The risk of errors, accidents and injuries has been found:

- to be higher on the night shift;
- to rise with increasing shift length over eight hours;
- to increase over successive shifts, especially if they are night shifts;
- to increase when there are not enough breaks.[18,22]

32 Poorly designed work schedules causing fatigue-induced impairment of performance will increase the risks. For example, a long night shift without breaks after a succession of previous night shifts will increase the likelihood of errors, accidents and injuries.

33 It is important not to underestimate the potential risk for serious fatigue-related errors and accidents. Sleepiness is thought to be the cause of up to one in five accidents on major roads in the UK,[23] contributing significantly to the approximate 3000 road deaths recorded annually.[24] After young men, shift workers are considered to be the category of drivers most at risk from accidents and, compared to day workers, night workers are more likely to be involved in accidents while driving home from work.[25]

34 Fatigue, night work and/or shift-working arrangements have been cited as major contributory factors in numerous well-documented accidents and incidents including Three Mile Island in 1979, Bhopal in 1984, Challenger Space Shuttle in 1986, Chernobyl in 1986, Clapham Junction in 1988 and Exxon Valdez in 1989.[26,27]

Health effects

35 As well as chronic fatigue, there is some evidence associating long-term exposure to shift work and the following ill health effects:[28-31]

- gastrointestinal problems such as indigestion, abdominal pain, constipation, chronic gastritis and peptic ulcers;
- cardiovascular problems such as hypertension, coronary heart disease;
- increased susceptibility to minor illnesses such as colds, flu and gastroenteritis.

36 Reproductive problems in female shift workers have also been reported.[32] While the association for reproductive effects is less strong, it would be wise to consider shift work, especially night shifts, as a potential risk to reproduction. Research into a possible link between shift work and breast cancer has been inconclusive.[33]

37 Shift work may also exacerbate existing health problems such as diabetes, asthma, epilepsy and psychiatric illness. Moreover, the effectiveness and potential toxicity of some drugs may vary depending on the time they are taken as the dose-response patterns of many drugs follow a circadian pattern.[28,31]

38 Shift workers, particularly those who work at night, may be at risk of ill health because shift work can disrupt our body clock (by interfering with the production of hormones by the body), disturb sleep and cause fatigue. In recognition of the particular risks to night workers, the WTR include a right for these workers to receive free health assessments.[1,34]

39 Individual and social factors may also contribute to the risk of ill health effects.[35-37] Consequently, not everyone will experience or have the same pattern or degree of health problems. An individual's attitude, behaviour, lifestyle, age, sex and family history plus the conditions they work in, will all play a part.

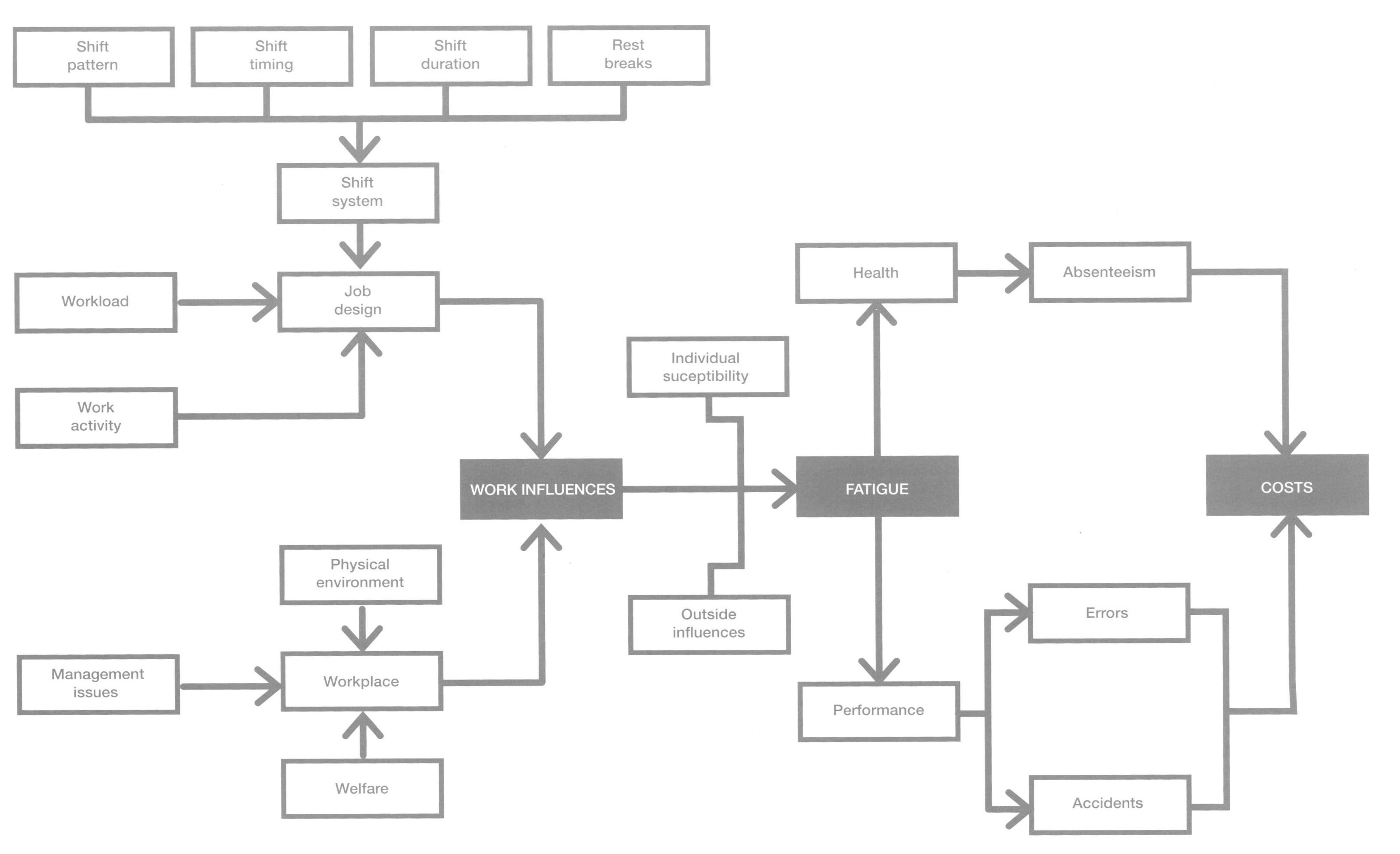

Figure 2 The causes and consequences of fatigue (after Folkard et al, 2003) [38]

Disruption of family and social life

40 A happy social and domestic life is an important foundation for health and well-being. The amount and quality of time spent with family and friends can, however, be affected by unusual patterns of work.[14, 30] A worker who experiences a disrupted social or domestic life may feel isolated, moody or depressed, which can affect their health and performance at work.

41 A work schedule that clashes with domestic responsibility can lead to a compromise between routines suited to work and those suited to less conflict at home. Shift workers, especially those who are primary carers, may spend more time with their family or fulfilling their domestic duties at the cost of sleep.[39] This will result in fatigue and its consequent implications for health and safety.

Individual susceptibility to the effects of shift work on health and well-being

42 Individuals vary in their tolerance to shift work, because:

- some find it easier to fall asleep, sleep for longer and adapt more easily to changes in sleep patterns;
- they may feel more alert at particular times of the day, eg some people could be described as 'night owls', others as 'larks';
- the ability to adapt to shift work decreases with age;
- they have differing degrees of health and fitness;
- they use different behaviours or coping strategies;
- they organise their domestic duties and social activities in line with their shifts.[35-37, 40]

43 While we cannot change our inbuilt characteristics or halt the ageing process, it is possible to adopt coping strategies, alter behaviour and make lifestyle changes that improve sleep quality, increase alertness and reduce health risks.[41] See Appendix 2 for strategies and practical advice shift workers can use to improve their health and well-being.[42]

Consider the costs and benefits of effective management of shift-working arrangements

44 Implementing a shift-work system or changing current shift-working arrangements can be a costly and time-consuming process. Workers may be resistant to changes in their working arrangements. While some workers may benefit from the proposed changes, other workers may consider themselves disadvantaged. For this reason, it is important to consult workers and their safety representatives and gain their agreement before making any changes to working arrangements.

45 It is important to recognise that a planned and systematic approach to assessing and managing the risks of shift work can improve the health and safety of workers. Reducing the problems associated with shift work may also financially benefit your business and society in general by:

- lowering sickness and absenteeism;
- decreasing lost-time incidents;
- reducing the risk of fatigue-related accidents;
- reducing the likelihood of compensation claims;
- increasing work efficiency;
- improving product quality;
- reducing staff turnover.

Establish systems to manage the risks of shift work

Seek management commitment to control the risks of shift work

46 Effective management of the risks associated with shift work requires commitment from senior management. It is vitally important to make sure senior management (ie those who make the business decisions, allocate funds and create a drive for change) are included in the development of, and/or modification of, shift-working arrangements.

47 Developing clear policies and procedures for managing shift-working arrangements ensures that people throughout the organisation, no matter how large or small, are aware that preventing or limiting the risks of shift working needs to be considered at all levels of planning.

Identify individuals responsible for shift-working arrangements

48 Depending on the size of the organisation, it may be appropriate to appoint one or more individuals to take responsibility for managing the risks associated with shift work. Broadening their knowledge about shift work and their familiarisation with appropriate health and safety policy and legislation will help develop a positive environment for dealing with shift-working arrangements. See Appendix 4 for sources of further information and help.

Involve safety representatives and workers

49 By law, employers must consult with employees on health and safety matters. So it is critical to consult and involve the shift workers themselves in discussions about how the management of shift work might affect health and safety. Involving a broad spectrum of the workforce in the decision-making process promotes a culture of openness. This will make workers more likely to accept changes and adopt a new shift-work schedule or different ways of working.

50 One way to involve workers and other stakeholders with an interest in shift-work arrangements is to establish a working group. This is a way of ensuring that different views and opinions are discussed. For example, you might wish to include:

- workers;
- safety representatives;
- a trade union representative;
- a supervisor or middle manager;
- an occupational health advisor;
- a health and safety officer (if applicable);
- a senior manager.

51 Alternatively, you may use other ways of consulting your employees or already have appropriate consultation procedures in place in your organisation.

Assess the risks associated with shift work in your workplace

Consider the risks that workers may be exposed to

52 Employers should carry out a suitable and sufficient assessment of the risks associated with shift work as part of your organisation's health and safety management system. You should record and review the risk assessment periodically and whenever changes to shift-working arrangements are considered or made.

53 A risk assessment requires an employer to consider risk factors at work and those who might be harmed by them. The risk assessment should take full account of the hazards associated with fatigue, and the likelihood of fatigue occurring because of shift working. To do this you need to gather and evaluate information about current shift-work arrangements in your organisation. You can then use the risk assessment to decide what you need to do to reduce the risks.

Establish who might be harmed by shift work

54 The risk factors summarised in the following sections are general and apply to most shift-work schedules. There may, however, be other risk factors that only apply to your industry sector. So, it is important to think about any additional risk factors of shift-work design in your organisation.

55 For example, while all workers are potentially at risk from shift work, you should consider certain groups who are more vulnerable than others. These include:

- young workers;
- older workers;
- new and expectant mothers;
- workers with pre-existing health conditions, which may be made worse by shift work, such as those with gastro-intestinal problems, coronary heart disease and sleeping problems;
- workers taking time-dependent medication such as insulin;
- temporary and other workers, such as sub-contractors and maintenance workers, who may not be familiar with or be able to adhere to current shift work schedules, or who have been on a different schedule with a previous employer;
- workers, who following a standard day's work, have remained on call through the subsequent night or weekend.[35-37]

56 You should also consider members of the public in your risk assessment, as there may be a risk they could be harmed as a result of accidents and catastrophes in which poor shift-work arrangements are a contributing factor.

57 To assess the risks, you will need to gather data about the shift-work arrangements in your organisation and use it to identify areas where you can make improvements, if necessary. Responsibility for deciding how to gather data should be made during your preparation and ideally agreed by those in your organisation who have an interest in shift-work arrangements. You will also need to assess how severe any risk factors are, record your findings and recognise that where there are several risk factors, the likelihood of fatigue-related problems will be increased.

58 Identifying issues associated with shift work can be difficult because there are many contributory factors that may affect your employees. So, it is advisable, to use a variety of information-gathering techniques to try to identify any common trends or patterns. For example, examining ill health, accident, absence, productivity and overtime records, direct observation of shift workers and using assessment tools and techniques (see Appendix 3) may be valuable. Common patterns, such as an increased accident rate or reduced production quality/quantity at certain times of day or over certain periods, may be symptoms of fatigue and poor shift-work design, but also consider other factors such as work load and work activity.

Consult workers and their safety representatives

59 It is very important to consult the shift workers and their safety representatives in the risk assessment process, as they have a clear interest in the matter and a direct knowledge of the advantages and disadvantages of existing work patterns. Keep records of any interviews or discussions for future reference.

60 Employing a number of different aids and techniques can stimulate discussion and help planning. For example, you could:

- encourage workers to share their experiences of shift work;
- discuss which shifts are hardest and why;
- use assessment tools and techniques to highlight potential problems and compare different shift schedules (see Appendix 3);
- provide examples of different shift-work schedules;
- invite spontaneous contribution of ideas.

61 You will need to handle any detailed risk assessment sensitively. Employees have a duty to help you to gather information and help with the assessment of risks associated with work. But, they also have rights to privacy and cannot be forced to co-operate in answering questionnaires or taking part in surveys. Even if your intentions are good, employees may not see it that way. The best policy is to explain what you are doing and your reasons for doing it. This is why involving workers and their safety representatives from an early stage is vital for a successful outcome.

Take action to reduce the risks

Assess how severe the risks are and identify where improvements need to be made

62 Tables 1-10 outline how different elements of your shift-work schedule and/or workplace environment might contribute to fatigue and other shift work-related problems. They also offer advice on how to control risks. Tables 11-12 summarise the current advice on controlling risks from shift work in the form of good practice guidelines.

63 Having identified the shift-work risk factors in your organisation, you then need to consider and prioritise where to make improvements. If you identify a number of issues, consider if it would be best to design a new schedule.

64 You may find it useful to use assessment tools such as HSE's Fatigue and Risk Index Tool, to identify whether any particular aspect of an existing or proposed working time pattern is likely to increase the risk of fatigue. See Appendix 3 for further details about the Fatigue and Risk Index Tool and other tools and techniques for assessing the risks associated with shift work.

65 To balance the health and safety needs of the workers and the demands of the organisation, apply the good practice guidelines when designing or modifying shift-working arrangements, where appropriate and where reasonably practicable.

Improve the shift-work schedule

66 There are many different shift-work schedules and each schedule has different features. This sheer diversity of work and workplaces mean that there is no single optimal shift system that suits everyone. Tables 1-7 summarise current knowledge and opinion on the various factors that contribute to the design of shift-work schedules and provide practical advice for reducing the risks of shift work.

67 Where relevant, information relating to the legal requirements of WTR is also included in the tables. However, complying with WTR may not in itself be enough to prevent fatigue and it is not enough to rely solely on these requirements to make sure you meet your obligations regarding health and safety in shift work.

68 Consideration of the factors that contribute to the design of shift-work schedules and addressing their associated risks will help you to reduce the risks that your employees are exposed to by shift work.

Table 1 Workload

Workload	Comments	Advice
Mental and physical demands	Workers with an appropriate workload will be more efficient, effective and less fatigued than those who are overburdened or have too little to do. Concentration and productivity tend to decline towards the end of the shifts, following lunch and during the night and early hours of the morning.	When planning work, plan an appropriate workload, according to the length and the timing of the shift. If practical, schedule demanding work for periods when workers are most alert and least likely to be fatigued. Where possible, demanding, dangerous and/or safety-critical work should be avoided during the night and early hours of the morning and towards the end of long shifts. When work is particularly demanding, consider shortening the length of the shift.

Table 2 Work activity

Work activity	Comments	Advice
Work Activity	Variation in work activity across a shift can help to relieve fatigue, especially where the worker has a range of tasks to complete, each with differing mental and physical demands. Rotating routine sedentary mental tasks with physical tasks can promote alertness or conversely help to relieve physical fatigue.	Where possible, schedule a variety of tasks into the shift plan and if practicable, allow workers some choice regarding their order of completion.

Table 3 Shift pattern

Shift pattern	Comments	Advice
Permanent shifts	Regular shifts allow a worker to adjust to a shift schedule to a certain degree, although any adjustment of the internal body clock will be lost during rest days if they revert to a normal diurnal cycle. Permanent night workers and early morning workers run the risk of chronic sleep debt, fatigue, ill health and disruption of family and social life.	Permanent night shifts should be avoided where possible, although some workers and supervisors may find them desirable. Ensure staff, especially those who work permanent night shifts or early morning shifts are aware of the risks, through provision of training and information.
	Regular shifts allow workers to plan domestic and social activities. They are appealing to some workers but others may prefer the flexibility of rotating shifts.	If reasonably practicable, offer workers the choice between permanent and rotating shifts.
	Can create strong healthy bonds within shift teams, but may also encourage less healthy attitudes or behaviours to develop, which could lead to a team making bad or irrational decisions.	Ensure there is enough supervision of shifts to facilitate communication between workers and promote appropriate behaviour and rational decision making.
	There may be poor communication due to limited contact between different shift teams.	Improve communication at shift handover to ensure that new shift teams are fully aware of issues that have arisen during the previous shift.
Rotating shifts	Rotating shift schedules reduce the number of nights an individual has to work, as night work is shared between all workers. However, the constantly changing shift pattern means that workers may have difficulty adapting to the schedule. The direction and speed of rotation can influence how an individual adapts to rotating shifts.	
Forward versus backward rotation	There is limited evidence that the internal body clock adapts more quickly to forward-rotating schedules, eg those where the worker progresses from morning to afternoon to night shifts in a clockwise direction.	Adopting forward-rotating schedules rather than backward-rotating, may help reduce sleep loss and fatigue.
	Changes from an early shift to a later shift may result in reduced rest time compared to a backward-rotating schedule.	Ensure there is adequate rest time between shifts. Under the WTR, the minimum time allowed between shifts is 11 hours.

Table 3 Shift pattern (continued)

Shift rotation	Comments	Advice
Fast rotation versus slow rotation	Fast rotation of shifts minimises disruption of the internal body clock and there is little to no adaptation to night shifts/early morning starts. Consequently direction of rotation may be less relevant for rapidly rotating shift schedules than for slowly rotating where there is some adjustment of the internal body clock.	Rotating shifts every 2-3 days is recommended, as the internal body clock does not adapt and sleep loss can be quickly recovered, reducing the risk of fatigue and ill health.
	Weekly/fortnightly rotating shifts are the most disruptive schedule as the internal body clock starts to adapt and then has to reset itself as the shift changes.	Weekly/fortnightly rotating shift schedules are not recommended. Avoid these where possible.
	Slow rotation of shifts maximises adaptation of the internal body clock, although there is a risk of sleep loss and fatigue. Any adjustment of the internal body clock to nights/early starts will be lost during rest days.	If fast rotation is not possible, then slowly rotating shifts over at least a 3-week period is the next best option.

Table 4 Shift timing

Shift timing	Comments	Advice
Night shifts	Night shifts disrupt the internal body clock and night workers are likely to suffer from sleep loss, poor quality sleep and fatigue, which may cause ill health. Fatigue may also increase the risk of errors and accidents, especially during the night, when people are less alert.	Only a limited number of workers can successfully adapt to night work. Try to find alternatives to night work for those workers who cannot adapt. Where possible, permanent night shifts should be avoided.
	Physically and/or mentally demanding or monotonous work will increase the risk of fatigue.	Consider the type of work being done and the workload. Where possible, avoid demanding, monotonous, dangerous and/or safety-critical work during the night and early hours of the morning.
	Night work increases the risk of ill health and disrupts family and social life.	Provide training and information about the risks of shift work for workers and their families. Make staff aware of sources of information and support, such as child care and counselling services. Under the WTR, night workers have a right to receive free health assessments.
	Working at night may limit access to training, development and workplace facilities such as staff restaurants, first aid and occupational health services.	Where reasonably practicable, provide similar facilities and opportunities for night workers as those available for your daytime workers.

Table 4 Shift timing (continued)

Shift timing	Comments	Advice
Early morning starts	Although less disruptive than night work, early morning starts can also reduce sleep and increase the risk of fatigue and ill health. Commuting times and availability of public transport may contribute to the fatigue related to early starts.	Where early morning starts are not essential for business needs, avoid shift starts before 07.00 am. Consider if providing transport to and from the workplace would be beneficial.
	Ability to sleep may be low in the early evening when the mind is alert and family and social commitments are competing. Loss of sleep may result in fatigue.	Provide training and information about the risks of shift work for workers and their families. Make staff aware of sources of information and support, such as child care and counselling services.
Afternoon starts	Risk of fatigue, ill health and accidents is lower than that from night as there is less disruption to the internal body clock. Performance does not appear to suffer unduly in comparison with day shifts.	Afternoon shifts are suitable for most workers and where practicable, you should adopt them in preference to night or early morning shifts.
	Workers who start work in the afternoon often sleep more than workers on other shift types. Afternoon starts can however reduce family and social contact.	Provide training and information about the risks of shift work for workers and their families. Make staff aware of sources of information and support such as child care and counselling services.
Daytime shifts	Preferred shift because it does not disrupt the internal body clock.	Where practicable, adopt day shifts rather than night or early morning shifts.

Table 5 Shift duration

Shift duration	Comments	Advice
8-hour shifts	8-hour shifts are considered to be the optimum length for sustained and consistent work. They allow more time for rest and completion of daily activities, but are generally less popular as there are fewer work-free days per week than with12-hour shifts.	There are few differences in the effects of 8-hour and 12-hour shifts on workers and there are no clear advantages to either system. However, the nature of the work needs to be considered. 8-hour shifts are preferable when work is monotonous, demands concentration or vigilance, is isolated, is safety critical and/or there is exposure to work-related physical or chemical hazards.
12-hour shifts	12-hour shifts are popular as they make the working week shorter and may offer some advantages over 8-hour shifts in terms of sleep, health and well-being. The perceived social benefits can lead to workforces tending to choose such shift lengths and patterns. However, workers have a limited mental and physical resource, which is dependent on their current state of fatigue and the type and duration of the job they are doing. Fatigue, especially towards the end of a long shift or during the night may reduce productivity and increase the risk of accidents.	Avoid shifts that are longer than 8 hours, where work is demanding, safety critical or monotonous and/or there is exposure to work-related physical or chemical hazards. Encourage and promote the benefit of frequent and regular breaks to reduce the risk of fatigue. Allow adequate recovery time between shifts and bear in mind that commuting times and availability of public transport may contribute to the fatigue related to long shifts. Limit 12-hour night shifts to 2-3 consecutive nights.

Table 5 Shift duration (continued)

Shift duration	Comments	Advice
12-hour shifts	Longer shifts may increase the risk of fatigue and ill health in vulnerable groups such as older workers and new and expectant mothers.	Consider the needs of vulnerable workers: arrange for these workers to do shorter shifts if necessary.
	Any advantages of 12-hour shifts in terms of health and well-being are likely to be lost if workers take on overtime or second jobs during their free time.	Shifts should not be planned to be longer than 12 hours. Avoid overrun and discourage overtime. Monitor and control shift swapping. Make adequate arrangements to cover absentees. Discourage workers from taking second jobs. If this is a particular problem you could set this as a condition of employment in contracts of work.
	As fewer shift teams are required for a 12-hour than for an 8-hour shift schedule it may be more difficult to arrange cover for illness, holidays, training and overtime.	Make adequate arrangements to cover absentees. Some companies include an extra shift in their rosters (usually days) to allow flexibility and time for training, development etc. Monitor and control shift swapping.
Shifts longer than 12 hours	Alertness and performance can significantly deteriorate over long shifts, which may increase the risk of errors and accidents.	Avoid shifts that are longer than 12 hours in length. Avoid overrun and discourage overtime. Monitor and control shift swapping. Make adequate arrangements to cover absentees. Discourage workers from taking second jobs.
Variable shift lengths	Variable shift lengths can give some of the free time benefits of longer workdays and may be less fatiguing. They are proving an increasingly popular compromise to the 8-hour vs 12-hour debate.	Consider if shifts of variable duration and/or flexible start and end times could offer a suitable compromise for your organisation. Bear in mind that schedule design will be more complex and require more planning and organisation.
Split shifts	Split shifts, where an individual's daily work is divided into two or more shifts, are unpopular as they lengthen the working day. The risk of fatigue is increased if there is too short a break between shifts to warrant a return home.	If reasonably practicable, avoid split shifts, as they do not allow enough recovery time between shifts. If split shifts are necessary, ensure that suitable on-site catering and rest facilities are available.
	Early starts coupled with late finishes can result in fatigue, ill health and disruption of family and social life.	Ensure workers are aware of the risks of shift work, through provision of training and information.

Table 6 Rest breaks within shifts

Rest breaks within shifts	Comments	Advice
	The risk of fatigue-related problems is higher towards the end of a shift and also during the night. Frequent short breaks can reduce fatigue, improve productivity and may reduce the risk of errors and accidents, especially when the work is demanding or monotonous.	Encourage and promote the benefit of frequent and regular breaks to reduce the risk of fatigue. Under the WTR, workers are entitled to a 20-minute rest break if the working day is longer than six hours. But consider the length of the shift and the workload when planning the amount and length of breaks. A short break of 5-15 minutes every 1-2 hours may help maintain performance and reduce accidents, particularly when the work is demanding or monotonous.
	Depending on the nature of the work, allowing workers some choice about how long and how often their breaks are may reduce fatigue and increase productivity. For example, a worker may benefit from more frequent breaks towards the end of a shift as fatigue sets in. When work is machine-paced rather than self-paced, introduction of frequent pre-planned rest breaks may increase productivity and reduce fatigue.	If practicable, workers should be allowed some discretion over when they take a break from work. Ideally, workers should be allowed to rest before they experience fatigue. However, workers may not always act as the best judge of when a break is needed and should be strongly discouraged from saving up their rest time in order to leave earlier. Where the pace is out of the worker's control (eg machine/system paced), schedule frequent rest breaks in the shift plan.
	A short period of sleep of around 20 minutes has been advocated by some as a way of coping with fatigue, especially on long shifts and on night shifts. However, if workers sleep for longer periods than this they may wake up feeling unrefreshed and less alert. This may decrease productivity and increase the risk of errors and accidents. When they wake up, workers may experience a short period (up to 15 minutes) of impaired alertness.	Napping should be well supervised and only be used as a strategy in organisations where there is a high risk of involuntary sleeping, such as driving and night-time vigilance tasks. Do not adopt it in work environments where important decisions, especially safety-critical decisions, could be clouded by sleepiness. If napping is adopted, appropriate facilities should be provided with scheduled breaks of around 40 minutes to allow workers sufficient time to have a short nap, refresh themselves and regain alertness before resuming work.
	A break taken away from the work station and/or work environment is considered to be more beneficial than those taken at the workstation.	Make facilities available and encourage workers to take their longer breaks away from their workstation.

Table 7 Rest breaks between shifts

Rest breaks between shifts	Comments	Advice
Rest periods between consecutive shifts	The risk of fatigue-related problems including ill health, errors and accidents increases when the break between the end of one shift and the start of the next shift is too short.	Workers need sufficient time between shifts to commute, eat meals, sleep and participate in domestic and social activities. Under WTR, the minimum time allowed between shifts is 11 hours.
Rest days	Too many consecutive work days can lead to an accumulation of fatigue and increase the risk of fatigue-related problems including ill health, errors and accidents. Sleep loss and fatigue can also build up if there are too many successive night shifts and/or early morning starts. The optimal number of successive workdays is unclear, as it depends on a number of factors including the shift pattern, the workload and the workplace environment.	In general, a limit of 5-7 consecutive working days should be set for standard (ie 7-8 hour) shifts. Where shifts are longer than this, for night shifts and for shifts with early morning starts it may be better to set a limit of 2-3 consecutive shifts, followed by 2-3 rest days to allow workers to recover.
	If there are a large number of rest days between successive shift schedules, lack of communication between workers and loss of familiarity with the work may increase the risk of errors and/or accidents.	Consider if regular refresher training in complex procedures and time allowed for refamiliarisation/updating would help when there are extended rest periods (including holidays) between successive shifts.
	Rest days are best when they allow the worker to recover from a work schedule, take part in social and domestic activities and if required, enable them to adjust to a new work schedule.	Under WTR, workers are entitled to a 24-hour day off per week, although days off may be averaged over a fortnight. When switching from day to night shifts or vice versa, make provision to allow workers a minimum of 2 nights of full sleep to enable them to adjust to the new schedule.
	Having free weekends is traditionally important to workers for social and domestic activities.	Where possible, regular weekend breaks should be built into the shift schedule.

Improve the workplace environment

69 Poor working conditions add to the risks of shift work and it is important to identify where improvements can be made. In many cases, changes to the workplace environment may be reasonably straightforward and easily introduced. However, it is important when you consider any alterations to consult and involve your employees and their safety representatives in the process.

70 Tables 8-10 outline how factors in the workplace environment may increase the risks associated with shift work and offer advice on how to make improvements to reduce these risks.

Table 8 Physical environment

Physical environment	Comments	Advice
Facilities	Shift working can isolate workers and prevent access to daytime workplace facilities such as staff restaurants, first aid, occupational health services, information and training.	Where reasonably practicable, provide similar facilities and opportunities for shift workers as those available for your daytime workers. Where this is not possible, it is important to make provision for workers to make a drink and heat up food and to allow workers to take their longer/meal breaks away from their workstation. First-aid facilities, and if possible, a trained first-aider should be made available for all shifts.
Lighting	Workplace lighting levels should be good enough to enable people to work, use workplace facilities and move from place to place in safety and to complete their tasks without the risk of eyestrain.	You should take into account the extent of natural lighting, the reflective properties of the surrounding area and the work materials, the nature of tasks being undertaken and the age of the workforce when you consider workplace lighting. A combination of direct and indirect lighting (eg uplighting) will help reduce glare and areas of shadow.
	Bright lights (> 6000 lux) have been shown to trigger changes in the internal body clock, which in turn may aid adaptation to night work by increasing alertness and reducing sleepiness	The practical application of bright light exposure to shift-work schedules is a complicated area. As yet it is relatively untried, and may require considerable resource. Seek specialist advice when considering this as a means of increasing alertness.
Temperature	The Workplace (Health, Safety and Welfare) Regulations 1992 (as amended)[43] lay down requirements for temperature in indoor workplaces. The associated Approved Code of Practice (ACOP) states that the temperature in work rooms should provide reasonable comfort without the need for special clothing. The minimum temperature should be at least 16°C, or 13°C if the work involves severe physical effort. A maximum temperature for work rooms is not specified. In addition to air temperature, the degree of ventilation, humidity and location of radiant heat sources will all affect the degree of comfort felt by workers.	Monitor workplace temperature on a regular basis to determine if adjustments to the heating supply need to be made for particular shifts. For example, during the night, heating may need to be increased to compensate for the drop in body temperature, however, a warm, stuffy atmosphere can cause drowsiness. Allow workers control of local heating arrangements. Where maintaining a comfortable temperature is impractical, take all reasonable steps to achieve a temperature which is as comfortable as possible. These may include providing localised heating/cooling devices, appropriate clothing and provision of rest facilities.

Table 9 Management issues

Management issues	Comments	Advice
Supervision	Under the HSW Act, employers must provide supervision as far as is reasonably practicable to ensure the health and safety at work of their employees. Good supervision of workers is vital for identifying potential hazards and ensuring compliance with health and safety rules. Employers should ensure that people responsible for shift-working arrangements, especially those in self-managed teams, have the competence and opportunity needed to fulfil this role. Supervisors can also play a key role in recognising problems associated with shift-working arrangements and identifying employees at risk of shift work-related problems.	Consider if increased supervision would be beneficial during key periods of low alertness, eg during the night and early hours of the morning, following lunch and towards the end of long shifts. Ensure supervisors are aware of the risks of shift work, through provision of training and information. Ensure that they are sufficiently trained to recognise the symptoms of fatigue, which may indicate that a worker is failing to cope with their current shift-work schedule or that there are general problems with the shift-working arrangements.
Overtime	Overtime, especially when following long shifts, is likely to increase the risk of fatigue-related problems including ill health, errors and accidents. Under-staffing, lack of flexibility for illness/absence cover, plant shutdown, pay incentives or personal convenience can lead workers to work extended hours and ignore recommended shift-work practice.	Where possible, avoid overtime by establishing systems to provide relief staff to cover absentees, vacancies, increased workloads and emergencies. If overtime is unavoidable, review a worker's preceding work and rest periods before agreeing to it. You should also monitor and record the hours that individuals have worked to identify where action should be taken to avoid excessive working hours. This is especially important when an individual has opted out of WTR, in workplaces where shift swapping is permitted and during exceptional circumstances such as emergency workers attending an incident.
Shift swapping	Uncontrolled shift swapping may increase the risk of fatigue-related problems including ill health, errors and accidents, especially if workers do double shifts or do not have enough time to rest between shifts.	Shift swapping should be monitored and recorded by supervisors. It is important to review a worker's scheduled work and rest periods before agreeing to a swap to avoid excessive hours being worked.
Standby and on-call duties	Workers who carry out standby and on-call duties have not entirely finished work and its related stresses, and whether actually called out or not, may experience disrupted and/or poor quality sleep and an accumulation of fatigue. Workers may be at risk of fatigue-related problems including ill health, errors and accidents if they are called into work, or have to remain at work following a shift.	Under WTR, periods when workers carrying out standby and on-call duties are required to be at the workplace, whether working or not, is considered working time. Make provision in the work schedule to allow adequate rest for those workers carrying out standby/on-call duties. Ensure workers are aware of the risks associated with fatigue through provision of training and information.

Table 9 Management issues (continued)

Management issues	Comments	Advice
Training and information	Training and information relating to shift work for shift workers and their families will increase understanding of the consequences of shift work and help workers to recognise fatigue-related problems and develop coping strategies. This may reduce fatigue-related ill health, improve productivity and reduce the risks of errors and accidents. However, training should not be relied on as the primary means of controlling risks from shift work. Ideally, training should complement other controls that have been put in place, such as improvements to the shift-work schedule and the workplace environment.	Tailored training and/or information regarding the risks associated with shift work should be available for workers, their families, their supervisors, safety representatives and management. Make workers aware of the potential impact fatigue may have on safety, health and well-being. Encourage workers to report shift work-related problems they may have and consider any suggestions workers make in relation to improving the shift-working arrangements. Encourage workers to take responsibility for their welfare outside work and promote the use of appropriate coping strategies to help workers and their families to adapt to shift work (see Appendix 2).
	Access to daytime training sessions may be limited, especially for those on permanent night shifts.	If possible, arrange/adapt training sessions to the shift pattern rather than restricting it to daytime hours. Alternatively, ensure that workers are given compensatory time off if they have to attend training during rest periods by establishing a system to provide relief staff when required. To help this, some companies include extra shifts in their rosters (usually on days) to allow flexibility and time for training and development.
Communication	Communication between workers can help to promote alertness, reduce the risk of errors and accidents and help prevent feelings of isolation.	Encourage interaction and if possible arrange for employees to work together or in teams. If an employee must work alone, encourage them to make contact with other workers at regular intervals. If they are located remotely then contact can be provided by telephone or similar communications devices. In case of emergency, provide an alarm or other communication device. Ensure information on workplace issues is made available to all staff.

Table 9 Management issues (continued)

Management issues	Comments	Advice
Communication	Handover of accurate, reliable information across shift changes is essential to ensure continuity of safe and effective working. Poor communication at shift handover may increase the risk of errors and accidents, particularly: ■ during plant maintenance; ■ when safety systems have been over-ridden; ■ during abnormal operations; ■ following lengthy absences from work; and ■ when handovers are between experienced and inexperienced staff. Adopting longer shifts can improve communication between successive shifts, as there are fewer handovers, however, this may be counterbalanced by an increased risk of fatigue-related problems and by the effects of extended rest periods on familiarity and skills.	Agree on, and make sure timing and procedures for transmitting information to the next shift team are clear, available to all staff and followed at all times. Avoid extending shifts by good planning of the handover, eg by building in a small overlap between start and finish times on consecutive shifts. Ideally, shift handovers should be conducted face-to-face and be two-way, with all participants taking responsibility for ensuring accurate communication, using both verbal and written means, be based on a pre-determined analysis of the information needs of incoming staff and be given as much time as necessary to ensure clear and accurate communication.

Table 10 Welfare

Welfare	Comments	Advice
Occupational health	A number of ill-health effects, including gastro-intestinal problems, cardiovascular disease, reproductive problems and increased susceptibility to minor illnesses have been associated with shift work.	Encourage workers to inform their doctor about their working arrangements, as this may help early diagnosis of any shift work-related ill health. Consider if alternative work is available for workers who have difficulties adapting to shift work or develop shift work-related health problems. This is particularly important for groups such as ageing workers and new and expectant mothers who might be more vulnerable to the risks of shift working.
	A fit and healthy workforce will be more resistant to stress and illness and may find it easier to adapt to shift work.	Promote healthy living strategies like increasing exercise and improving diet, such as those included in Appendix 2.

Table 10 Welfare (continued)

Welfare	Comments	Advice
Occupational health	Under WTR, employers are required to ensure that workers are fit for night work and must offer a free health assessment to anyone who is about to start working nights and to all night workers on a regular basis.	Employers should seek specialist advice from a suitably qualified health care professional, when devising and assessing the results of health assessments. If a worker suffers from health problems that are caused or made worse by night work, you should, where possible, transfer him or her to day work.
Lone working/violence	Shift workers, especially those who work alone or unsociable hours may be vulnerable to violence.	Employers should take steps to make sure that the workplace and its surroundings are well lit, safe and secure. Consider if shift start and end times can be adjusted to fit in with the availability of public transport. If not, consider providing transport to and from the workplace. Promote car sharing and ensure car parks and entrances are well lit and secure. Encourage communication between workers and ensure all, especially those who work alone, have access to telephones and alarm systems. Consider if you need to instal security cameras and/or provide security staff.

Apply good practice guidelines

71 The best advice currently available regarding shift-work schedule design and the workplace environment is summarised in Tables 11-12. Where reasonably practicable, you should follow these guidelines when designing or altering your shift-working arrangements. You may find the assessment tools and techniques listed in Appendix 3 useful when you consider any changes to your own particular shift-working arrangements.

72 These guidelines are general though, and cover a wide range of factors that may or may not be relevant to your particular sector. Guidelines and sector-specific standards of good practice have also been developed by some industrial sectors and may give you more ideas.

73 Given the wide variety of possible shift-working arrangements, it is necessary to use common sense when applying the good practice guidelines. For example during exceptional circumstances, there may be times when curtailing overtime and forcing a change of shift might be more risky than allowing workers to complete a task. Likewise, emergency workers may not always be able to take a scheduled break while attending a serious incident. In such cases, it is important to monitor and record the hours people have worked, to identify where to take action to avoid excessive hours being worked and that there are suitable arrangements to make sure workers are given compensatory time off following the incident.

74 You will also need to balance the good practice guidelines with the operational concerns of your own business. You will need to consider:

- your available resources, eg person hours available;
- how you use these resources, eg number of work groups, handovers between shifts;
- whether current resources are sufficient to support changes to the shift-working arrangements, eg do they meet the business demands?

75 Applying, where reasonably practicable, the good practice guidelines will help you reduce the risks that your employees are exposed to by shift working.

Table 11 Good practice guidelines for shift-work schedule design

Plan a workload that is appropriate to the length and timing of the shift.
If reasonably practicable, schedule a variety of tasks to be completed during the shift and allow workers some choice about the order they need to be done in.
Avoid scheduling demanding, dangerous, monotonous and/or safety-critical work during the night, early morning, towards the end of long shifts and during other periods of low alertness.
Avoid placing workers on permanent night shifts.
If possible, offer workers a choice between permanent and rotating shift schedules.
Where possible, adopt a forward-rotating schedule for rotating shifts rather than a backward-rotating schedule.
Either rotate shifts very quickly, eg every 2-3 days or slowly, eg every 3-4 weeks and avoid weekly/fortnightly rotating shift schedules.
If not strictly necessary for business needs, try to avoid early morning starts before 7.00 am.
Where possible, arrange shift start/end times to be convenient for public transport or consider providing transport for workers on particular shifts.
Limit shifts to a maximum of 12 hours (including overtime) and consider the needs of vulnerable workers.
Limit night shift or shifts where work is demanding, monotonous, dangerous and/or safety critical to 8 hours.
Consider if shifts of a variable length or flexible start/end times could offer a suitable compromise.
Avoid split shifts unless absoloutely necessary to meet business needs.
Encourage and promote the benefit of regular breaks away from the workstation.
Where possible, allow workers some discretion over when they take a break, but discourage workers from saving up break time in order to leave earlier.
In general, limit consecutive working days to a maximum of 5-7 days and make sure there is adequate rest time between successive shifts.
Where shifts are long (> 8 hours), for night shifts and for shifts with early morning starts, it may be better to set a limit of 2-3 consecutive shifts.
When switching from day to night shifts or vice versa, allow workers a minimum of 2 nights' full sleep.
Build regular free weekends into the shift schedule.

Table 12 Good practice guidelines for improving the shift-work environment

Provide similar facilities and opportunities for shift workers as those available for your daytime workers.
Ensure that workplace lighting is adequate and adjustable by workers.
Ensure that the workplace temperature is adjustable and allows workers to carry out their tasks in reasonable comfort.
Consider increasing supervision during key periods of low alertness, eg during the night, early morning, towards the end of long shifts and other periods of low alertness.
Make sure supervisors and team members with responsibility for shift-working arrangements are aware of the risks associated with shift work and can recognise shift work-related problems.
Control overtime and shift swapping by monitoring and recording hours worked and rest periods. Discourage workers from taking second jobs.
Make provision in the work schedule to allow adequate rest for those workers carrying out standby/on-call duties or overtime.
Provide training and information for workers, their families and management on the risks associated with shift work and on coping strategies. This may help workers to cope better with shift work.
Make provision to release staff for foreseeable training, development and communication needs.
Encourage interaction between workers and provide a means of communication for lone workers.
Agree on, and ensure timing and procedures for transmitting information to the next shift team are followed at all times.
Encourage workers to inform their doctor about their working arrangements.
Promote healthy living strategies such as increasing exercise and improving diet.
Ensure that free health assessments are provided for night workers.
Ensure that the workplace and its surroundings are well lit, safe and secure and that workers are free from the threat of violence.

Check and review your shift-work arrangements regularly

Implement a system for early reporting of problems associated with shift work

76 Assessing and managing the risks associated with shift work will improve the health and safety of workers by reducing the risks they are exposed to.This process will also help identify many of the problems associated with shift work. However, it is not always possible to prevent shift work-related problems and so it is very important to have systems in place for reporting and investigating any problems that may occur.

77 As some workers may be reluctant to report problems, it is vital that management and safety representatives emphasise and promote the benefits of early reporting. Key groups such as supervisors or shift managers can play a major role in this, if they are encouraged to report early. The reporting process should be simple and straightforward and make sure any problems are dealt with in a timely manner.

78 Where there are cases of ill health that may be associated with your shift-working arrangements, you may find it beneficial to seek advice from an occupational health professional who can determine if the complaint is related to work, provide advice on the nature of the complaint, its treatment and the potential for any long-term effects.

Monitor alterations to shift-work schedules and/or work conditions

79 Altering the design of your shift schedules and making changes to the shift-work environment may help solve some problems, but create others. It may take a number of changes and some time to get things right, so it is important to monitor and review any changes on a regular basis.

80 When making changes it is vitally important to consult your workers and explain what you are doing and your reasons for doing it. Involving them in the process makes the acceptance of changes to shift-working arrangements more likely.

81 To find out if changes to the shift-working arrangements have reduced risks, you will need to monitor and undertake a risk assessment both before and after any changes take place. This will help you set clear and measurable targets for improvement and identify if these have been met. Table 13 gives some general examples of indicators you could use to determine if changes have helped, however, you should also consider if there are other measures more suited to your particular sector.

82 To get a full picture, collect a mixture of objective and subjective information. For example, you could monitor worker's opinions on old and new shift-working arrangements by using focus groups, questionnaires, interviews and assessment tools.

83 You could also use recorded information such as ill health, accident, absence, productivity and overtime and shift-swapping records, as these are valuable sources of information. You may also find it helpful to make observations during each shift.

84 The more you do to assess the effectiveness of changes to the shift-working arrangements, the more likely you are to get things right. However, you should only do what is reasonably practicable for the size of your organisation.

Periodically review the effectiveness of your shift-working arrangements

85 It is important that you monitor and periodically review your shift-working arrangements to check they are still effective and do not impact on health and safety. You should also use these processes to enable a cycle of continuous improvement, which will help both your workers and your organisation.

Table 13 Issues and measures of success

Indicator	Examples of possible performance criteria (measures of success)
Fatigue	Use assessment tools such as HSE's Fatigue and Risk Index Tool to identify if changes in the shift-work schedule have reduced fatigue.
Sleepiness at work	Use assessment tools such as the 'Epworth sleepiness scale' to determine sleepiness.
Accidents, near misses and safety-critical events	Do records show a reduction in accidents, near misses and safety-critical events?
Absenteeism	Do records show a decrease in absenteeism?
Staff turnover	Do records show a decrease in staff turnover?
Employee welfare	Use focus groups, interviews, questionnaires and observation to determine if workers view the shift-working arrangements positively.
Performance and productivity	Do records show an increase in performance and/or productivity?
Company profits	Have profits increased since changes were made?

Appendix 1 Legal requirements

1 Employers have legal responsibilities to ensure the health and safety at work of their employees, and this includes removing or controlling the risks of fatigue by organising and planning shift-working arrangements. They also have a broader responsibility for the health and safety of others who might be affected by their work activities, which is another reason why it is important to control fatigue.

2 The Health and Safety at Work etc Act 1974 and the Management of Health and Safety at Work Regulations 1999 place general duties on employers and others in regard to managing the risks of shift work. There are also other regulations, which impose specific requirements on employers with regard to the number of hours worked and how these hours are scheduled. These include the Working Time Regulations 1998 (as amended) and other industry-specific legislation such as the Railway and Other Guided Transport Systems (Safety) Regulations 2006.

3 It is also a requirement under the Safety Representatives and Safety Committees Regulations and the Health and Safety (Consultation with Employees) Regulations 1996 that employers consult with employees on health and safety matters and take account of their views before reaching any decision.

Working Time Regulations Summary

4 The basic rights and protections that the Working Time Regulations 1998 (as amended) provide for workers are:

- a limit of an average of 48 hours a week which a worker can be required to work (though workers can choose to work more if they want to);
- for night workers, a limit of an average of 8 hours work in each 24-hour period;
- a right for night workers to receive free health assessments;
- a right to 11 hours consecutive rest a day;
- a right to a day off each week;
- a right to a rest break if the working day is longer than six hours;
- a right to four weeks' paid leave per year.

5 A worker is someone who has a contract of employment, or someone who is paid a regular salary or wage and works for an organisation, business or individual. A young worker is someone who is above the minimum school leaving age but under 18.

6 If you are self-employed, running your own business and are free to work for different clients and customers, the Working Time Regulations do not apply.

7 Certain workers are not subject to these Regulations, because they are/will be governed by sector-specific provisions. These are:

- sea transport, as covered by the Seafarers' Directive (1999/63/EC);
- mobile workers in inland waterways and lake transport;
- workers on board sea-going fishing vessels;
- air transport, as covered by the Aviation Directive (2000/79/EC).

8 Mobile workers in road transport are only subject to certain provisions of these Regulations. They are covered by the Road Transport Directive (2002/15/EC).

9 The armed forces, the police and emergency services are outside the scope of the Regulations in certain circumstances. However, young workers in the armed forces, the police and emergency services, the aviation sector and the road transport sector are covered by the young workers provisions in the Regulations.

10 Workers can agree to work longer than the 48-hour limit. An agreement must be in writing and signed by the worker. This is generally referred to as an opt-out. It can be for a specified period or an indefinite period. Employers cannot force a worker to sign an opt-out. Workers cannot be fairly dismissed or subjected to detriment for refusing to sign an opt-out.

11 Young workers may not ordinarily work more than 8 hours a day or 40 hours a week. These hours worked cannot be averaged out and there is no opt-out available. They should not ordinarily work at night, although there are certain exceptions.

12 To be sure workers are fit for night work, employers must offer a free health assessment to anyone who is about to start working nights and to all night workers on a regular basis. A night worker cannot opt-out of the night work limit. Where a night worker's work involves special hazards or heavy physical or mental strain, there is an absolute limit of eight hours on the worker's working time each day – this is not an average.

13 The limits and health assessments (if a night worker) are enforced by HSE, local authority environmental health departments, the Civil Aviation Authority and the Vehicle and Operator Services Agency. The entitlements to rest and leave are enforced through employment tribunals.

14 This is general guidance only and should not be regarded as a complete or authoritative statement of the law. The latest information can be found at: www.dti.gov.uk/employment/employment-legislation/working-time-regs/index.html.

Appendix 2
Strategies and practical advice shift workers can use to improve their health and well-being

Driving to and from work

1 Driving to and from work can be risky, particularly after a long shift, a night shift or before an early start. The following strategies may make driving safer:

- consider using public transport or taxis rather than driving;
- exercise briefly before your journey;
- share driving if possible;
- drive carefully and defensively;
- try not to hurry;
- stop if you feel sleepy and take a short nap if it is safe to do so;
- make occasional use of caffeine or energy drinks.

Identify a suitable sleep schedule

2 Most adults need 7-8 hours sleep a day, although this decreases with age. If you cannot do this, try to rest, as this is still beneficial. Recording sleep patterns and problems using a diary may help to explain fatigue and tiredness. It can also be used to help find the most suitable strategies and conditions for a better quality of sleep:

- if you work regular shifts, try going to bed at different times, eg soon after you arrive back from work or stay up and sleep before the next shift;
- have a short sleep before your first night shift;
- if coming off night shifts, have a short sleep and go to bed earlier that night;
- once you have identified a suitable sleep schedule, try to keep to it.

Make the environment favourable for sleeping

3 Sleep loss and fatigue are some of the most significant problems for shift workers. It is important to try and maintain your normal level of sleep and rest. Daytime sleep is usually lighter, shorter and of poorer quality than night time sleep. It is more frequently disturbed because of warmer temperatures and daytime noise. To help make the environment favourable for sleeping:

- sleep in your bedroom and avoid using it for other activities such as watching television, eating and working;
- use heavy curtains, blackout blinds or eye shades to darken the bedroom;
- disconnect the phone or use an answer machine and turn the ringer down;
- ask your family not to disturb you and to keep the noise down when you are sleeping;
- discuss your work pattern with close neighbours and ask them to try and avoid noisy activities during your sleep time;
- if it is too noisy to sleep consider using earplugs, white noise or background music to mask external noises;
- adjust the bedroom temperature to a comfortable level, cool conditions improve sleep.

Techniques to promote sleep

4 To promote sleeping, try to follow a similar routine to the one you follow before a normal night's sleep. The following tips may help you relax after a shift and promote sleep:

- go for a short walk, relax with a book, listen to music and/or take a hot bath before going to bed;
- avoid vigorous exercise before sleep as it is stimulating and raises the body temperature;
- avoid caffeine, 'energy' drinks and other stimulants a few hours before bedtime as they can stop you going to sleep;
- don't go to bed feeling hungry: have a light meal or snack before sleeping but avoid fatty, spicy and/or heavy meals, as these are more difficult to digest and can disturb sleep;
- avoid alcohol as it lowers the quality of sleep.

Diet

5 It is very important to consider the timing and quality of your meals. Digestive problems are common in shift workers, due to disruption of the internal body clock and poor diet. Plan your meals to help you stay alert at work and to relax/sleep when you need to rest:

- regular light meals/snacks are less likely to affect alertness or cause drowsiness than a single heavy meal;
- choose foods that are easy to digest such as pasta, rice, bread, salad, fruit, vegetables and milk products;
- avoid fatty, spicy and/or heavy meals as these are more difficult to digest. They can make you feel drowsy when you need to be alert. They may also disturb sleep when you need to rest;
- avoid sugary foods, such as chocolate - they provide a short-term energy boost followed by a dip in energy levels;
- fruit and vegetables are good snacks as their sugar is converted into energy relatively slowly and they also provide vitamins, minerals and fibre;
- drink plenty of fluid, as dehydration can reduce both mental and physical performance, but avoid drinking too much fluid before sleeping, as this may overload the bladder.

Stimulants and sedatives

6 Shift workers often turn to stimulants such as coffee or cigarettes to keep them awake and sedatives such as alcohol or sleeping pills to help them sleep. Avoid such aids, as they only have short-term effects on alertness as tolerance to their effects develops. Persistent use may also increase the risk of dependence:

- caffeine is a mild stimulant present in coffee, tea and cola as well as in tablet form and in special energy drinks. It can improve reaction time and feelings of alertness for short periods. Only use caffeine occasionally and don't rely on it to keep you awake. If you do decide to take caffeine or other stimulants, you should consider what might happen when its effects wear off, eg when you are operating machinery or driving.
- avoid the use of alcohol to help you fall asleep. Although alcohol can promote the onset of sleep it is also associated with earlier awakenings, disrupted sleep and poorer sleep quality. Regularly drinking too much increases the risk of long-term damage to your physical and mental health, your work, social and personal relationships.
- regular use of sleeping pills and other sedatives to help sleep are not recommended, because they can lead to dependency and addiction.
- new drugs have recently been developed that can alter our state of alertness. Although their use may be widespread abroad, the ways they work and their long-term effects are not yet fully understood. Consequently their use is not advised, unless under medical supervision.

Physical fitness and a healthier lifestyle

7 An unhealthy lifestyle combined with shift work may increase the likelihood of sleep disorders and sleep loss or exacerbate existing sleep problems. A good diet, regular meals and exercise can improve sleep quality, health and well-being:

- you can improve your fitness by spending 30 minutes a day on a physical activity including housework and walking. Consider joining a gym or taking part in a regular exercise class;
- eat healthy meals on a regular basis;
- cut down or give up smoking;
- reduce your alcohol intake;
- seek advice from your doctor, if you require regular medication such as insulin for diabetes or suffer from a chronic condition such as epilepsy.

Family and friends

8 Working shifts that differ from the routines of friends and family can leave you feeling isolated. It is important to make the effort not to lose contact with them:

- talk to friends and family about shift work. If they understand the problems you are facing it will be easier for them to be supportive and considerate;
- make your family and friends aware of your shift schedule, so they can include you when planning social activities;
- make the most of your time off and plan meal times, weekends and evenings together;
- plan your domestic duties around your shift schedule and try to ensure that you do not complete them at the cost of rest/sleep. You may need to change the times/days when some jobs are done;
- invite others who work similar shifts to join you in social activities when others are at work and there are fewer crowds.

Ways to improve your alertness at work

9 On some shifts, such as nights and very early mornings, you may find it difficult to remain alert and this can affect your performance. It may also increase the risk of mistakes, injury and accidents. You may find it helpful to:

- take moderate exercise before starting work which may increase your alertness during the shift;
- keep the light bright;
- take regular short breaks during the shift if possible;
- get up and walk around during breaks;
- plan to do more stimulating work at the times you feel most drowsy;
- keep in contact with co-workers, as this may help both you and them stay alert.

Appendix 3 Assessment tools and techniques

1 A number of tools and techniques are available, which may help you to assess the risks associated with shift work. Tools that assess the risks of particular shift schedules generally use mathematical modelling to assess the influence of factors such as time and duration of shift, number and length of rest breaks and rest days and cumulative fatigue (ie the build up of fatigue from sleep disruption).

2 HSE's Fatigue and Risk Index Tool contains two indices. The Fatigue Index incorporates factors known to be related to the build up of fatigue, including shift timing, shift duration, breaks, rest periods, cumulative fatigue (ie the build up of fatigue from sleep disruption) and the workload and its output relates to the probability of high levels of sleepiness. The Risk Index is based on occupational injury data and is expressed in terms of the relative risk of an incident occurring.

3 There are also a number of questionnaires/surveys available. These range from the very simple, such as the Epworth Sleepiness Scale, which provides a measure of an individual's general level of daytime sleepiness, to more complicated surveys, including the Standard Shiftwork Index and the Swedish Occupational Fatigue Inventory that have been developed for assessing large groups of individuals.

4 Other techniques that might also be valuable in the assessment and management of the risks associated with shift work include the use of sleep diaries, health assessments and employee education programmes.

Summary evaluation of tools used to estimate shift work-associated fatigue

Stone B M 2004 'Tools and techniques for estimating risks associated with shift work' *Rail Safety and Standards Board Human Factors Research Catalogue* CD-ROM 2004

HSE's Fatigue and Risk Index Tool

The development of a fatigue/risk index for shiftworkers RR446/2006 Available from www.hse.gov.uk/research/rrhtm/index.htm

An electronic version of the Fatigue and Risk Index Tool is available at www.hse.gov.uk/research/rrpdf/rr446cal.xls

The Epworth Sleepiness Scale

Johns M W 'A new method for measuring daytime sleepiness: The Epworth sleepiness scale' *Sleep* 1991 **14** (6) 540-545

The Standard Shiftwork Index

Barton J, Spelten E, Totterdell P et al 'The Standard Shiftwork Index: A battery of questionnaires for assessing shift-related problems' *Work and Stress* 1995 **9** (1), 4-30

Swedish Occupational Fatigue Inventory

Ahsberg E, Gamberale F and Kjelberg 'A Perceived Quality of Fatigue during Different Occupational Tasks. Development of a Questionnaire' *International Journal of Industrial Ergonomics* 1997 **20** (2) 121-135

Appendix 4
Further sources of information and help

Government bodies

Health and Safety Executive
Rose Court
2 Southwark Bridge
London SE1 9HS
Tel: 0845 345 0055
Fax: 0845 408 9566
e-mail: hse.infoline@natbrit.com
web: www.hse.gov.uk

Department of Trade and Industry
Response Centre
1 Victoria Street
London SW1H 0ET
Tel: 020 7215 5000
e-mail: dti.enquiries@dti.gsi.gov.uk
Website: www.dti.gov.uk

Department of Health
Richmond House
79 Whitehall
London SW1A 2NL
Tel: 020 7210 4850
e-mail: dhmail@dh.gsi.gov.uk
Website: www.dh.gov.uk

Professional societies whose membership includes experts in human performance, fatigue, shift work and human reliability

The Ergonomics Society
Elms Court
Elms Grove
Loughborough
Leicestershire LE11 1RG
Tel: 01509 234904
Fax: 01509 235666
e-mail: ergsoc@ergonomics.org.uk
Website: www.ergonomics.org.uk

The British Psychological Society
St Andrews House
48 Princess Road East
Leicester LE1 7DR
Tel: 0116 254 9568
Fax: 0116 247 0787
e-mail: enquiry@bps.org.uk
Website: www.bps.org.uk

The Society of Occupational Medicine
6 St Andrews Place
Regents Park
London NW1 4LB
Tel: 020 7486 2641
Fax: 020 7486 0028
e-mail: admin@som.org.uk
Website: www.som.org.uk

The British Occupational Health Society
5/6 Melbourne Business Court
Millennium Way
Derby DE24 8LZ
Tel: 01332 298101
Fax: 01332 298099
e-mail: admin@bohs.org
Website: www.bohs.org

Other organisations with an interest in human performance, fatigue, shift work and human reliability

The Royal Society for the Prevention of Accidents
RoSPA House, Edgbaston Park,
353 Bristol Road, Edgbaston,
Birmingham B5 7ST
Tel: 0121 248 2000
Fax: 0121 248 2001
email: help@rospa.com
Website: www.rospa.co.uk

The Working Time Society
AUDI AG I/SG-1
D-85045 Ingolstadt
Germany
Tel: +49 841 89 32148
Fax: +49 841 89 35838
e-mail: sonia.hornberger@audi.de
Website: www.workingtime.org

European Foundation for the Improvement of Living and Working Conditions
Wyattville Road, Loughlinstown
Dublin 18, Ireland
Tel: +353 1 2043100
Fax: +353 1 2826456
e-mail: postmaster@eurofound.eu.int
Website: www.eurofound.eu.int

Advisory, Conciliation and Arbitration Service (ACAS)
Brandon House
180 Borough High Street
London, SE1 1LW
Tel: 08457 47 47 47
Website: www.acas.org.uk

Trades Union Congress
Congress House
Great Russell Street
London, WC1B 3LS
Tel: 020 7636 4030
Fax: 020 7636 0632
e-mail: info@tuc.org.uk
Website: www.tuc.org.uk

Appendix 5
References and further reading

References

1 *The Working Time Regulations 1998 (as amended)* SI1998/1833 The Stationery Office1998 ISBN 0 11 079410 9

2 Department of Trade and Industry *Your Guide to the Working Time Regulations: Workers and Employers* Available online at www.dti.gov.uk/er/work_time_regs/wtr0.htm

3 Office of Rail Regulation 2006 *The Railways and other Guided Transport Systems (Safety) Regulations 2006*

4 Office of Rail Regulation Guidance on *Managing fatigue in safety-critical work* is in preparation. it will be available online at www.rail-reg.gov.uk

5 *Health and Safety at Work etc Act 1974 (c.37)* The Stationery Office 1974 ISBN 0 10 543774 3

6 *Management of health and safety at work. Management of Health and Safety at Work Regulations 1999. Approved Code of Practice and guidance* L21 (Second edition) HSE Books 2000 ISBN 0 7176 2488 9

7 *Safety representatives and safety committees* L87 (Third edition) HSE Books 1996 ISBN 0 7176 1220 1

8 *A guide to the Health and Safety (Consultation with Employees) Regulations 1996. Guidance on Regulations* L95 HSE Books 1996 ISBN 0 7176 1234 1

9 *Consulting employees on health and safety: A guide to the law* Leaflet INDG232 HSE Books 1996 (single copy free or priced packs of 15 ISBN 0 7176 1615 0)

10 Advisory, Conciliation and Arbitration Service *Changing patterns of work* ACAS Publications 2002 ACAS Advisory Booklet No B09

11 McOrmond T 'Changes in working trends over the last decade' *Labour Market Trends* 2004 112 (1) 25-35

12 Office for National Statistics *Labour Force Survey 1992-2005* The Stationery Office 2005

13 *Successful health and safety management* HSG65 (Second edition) HSE Books 1997 ISBN 0 7176 1276 7

14 Monk T H and Folkard S *Making shiftwork tolerable* Taylor and Francis 1992

15 Smith C S, Folkard S and Fuller J A 'Shiftwork and Working Hours' in *Handbook of Occupational Health Psychology* 2003 163-183 Washington DC: American Psychological Association

16 Minors D S and Waterhouse J M 'Circadian rhythms in general' *Occupational Medicine* 1990 **5**(2) Pennsylvania USA: Hanley and Belfus

17 Åkerstedt T, Czeisler C, Dinges D F et al 'Accidents and Sleepiness: A consensus statement from the International Conference on Work hours, Sleepiness and Accidents' *Journal of Sleep* 1994 **3** 19

18 Folkard S and Tucker P 'Shift work, safety and productivity' *Occupational Medicine* 2003 **53** (2) 95-101

19 Krueger G P 'Sustained work, fatigue, sleep loss and performance: A review of the issues' *Work and Stress* 1989 **3** (2) 129-141

20 Harrison Y and Horne J M 'The impact of sleep deprivation on decision making: A review' *Journal of Experimental Psychology: Applied* 2000 **6** (3) 236-249

21 Kroemer K E H and Grandjean E *Fitting the task to the human: A textbook of Occupational Ergonomics* (Fifth edition) Taylor and Francis1997

22 Folkard S, Lombardi D A and Tucker P 'Shiftwork: Safety, sleepiness and sleep' *Industrial Health* 2005 **43**, 20-23

23 Horne J A and Reyner L A 'Vehicle accidents related to sleep: A review' *Occupational and Environmental Medicine* 1999 **56** (5) 289-294

24 Department for Transport/Office for National Statistics *Road Casualties Great Britain: 2004* The Stationery Office 2004 ISBN 0 11 522703 6 Available online at www.dft.gov.uk/stellent/groups/dft_transstats/documents/downloadable/dft_transstats_041304.pdf

25 Royal Society for the Prevention of Accidents *Driver Fatigue And Road Accidents. A Literature Review And Position Paper* 2001 Available online at www.rospa.com/roadsafety/info/fatigue.pdf

26 Mittler M M, Carskadon M A, Czeisler C A et al 'Catastrophes, Sleep and Public Policy: Consensus Report' *Sleep* 1988 **11** (1) 100-109

27 Dinges D F 'An overview of sleepiness and accidents' *Journal of Sleep Research* 1995 **4** (S2) 4-14

28 Costa G 'The impact of shift and night work on health' *Applied Ergonomics* 1996 **27** 9-16

29 European Foundation for the Improvement of Living and Working Conditions *Shiftwork and Health* Office for official publications of the European Communities, Bulletin of European studies on time No 1/2000 2000

30 Harrington J M 'Health effects of shiftwork and extended hours of work' *Occupational and Environmental Medicine* 2001 **58** 68-72

31 Knutsson A 'Health disorders of shift workers' *Occupational Medicine* 2003 **53** (2) 103-108

32 Nurminen T 'Shift work and reproductive health' *Scandinavian Journal of Work, Environment and Health* 1998 **24** (S3), 28-34

33 *Shift work and breast cancer: a critical review of the epidemiological evidence* HSE 2003 Available online at www.hse.gov.uk/research/rrhtm/index.htm

34 Society of Occupational Medicine *Guidance on the Provision of Health Assessments Under the Working Time Regulations 1998* Society and Faculty of Occupational Medicine 1999

35 Härmä M 'Ageing, physical fitness and shiftwork tolerance' *Applied Ergonomics* 1996 **27** (1) 25-29

36 Nachreiner F 'Individual and social determinants of shiftwork tolerance' *Scandinavian Journal of Work, Environment and Health* 1998 **24** (S3) 35-42

37 Costa G 'Factors influencing health of workers and tolerance to shift work' *Theoretical Issues in Ergonomics Science* 2003 **4** (3-4) 263-288

38 Folkard S, Sutton L and Yates A 'Impact of shiftwork on fatigue' *Rail Safety and Standards Board Human Factors Research Catalogue* CD-ROM 2003

39 Loudoun R J and Bohle P L 'Work/non-work conflict and health in shiftwork: Relationships with family status and social support' *The International Journal of Occupational and Environmental Health* 1997 **3** (3), S71-S77

40 Costa G 'Shift work and occupational medicine: An overview' *Occupational Medicine* 2003 **53** (2) 83-88

41 Knauth P and Hornberger S 'Preventative and compensatory measures for shift workers' *Occupational Medicine* 2003 **53** (2) 109-116

42 National Institute for Occupational Safety and Health *Plain Language about Shiftwork* 1997 Available online at www.cdc.gov/niosh/publistd.html

43 *Workplace health, safety and welfare. Workplace (Health, Safety and Welfare) Regulations 1992. Approved Code of Practice* L24 HSE Books 1992 ISBN 0 7176 0413 6

Further reading

Other sources of information used in the production of this guidance

Ahasan R, Lewko J, Campbell, D et al 'Adaptation to night shifts and synchronisation processes of night workers' *Journal of Physiological Anthropology* 2001 **20** (4) 215-226

Åkerstedt T 'Shift work and disturbed sleep/wakefulness' *Occupational Medicine* 2003 **53** (2) 89-94

Åkerstedt T, Klecklund G, Gillberg M et al 'Sleepiness and days of recovery' *Transportation Research* 2000 **F3** 251-261

Bonnefond A, Tassi P, Roge J et al 'A critical review of techniques aiming at enhancing and sustaining worker's alertness during the night shift' *Industrial Health* 2004 **42** 1-14

Burgess H J, Sharkey K M and Eastman C I 'Bright light, dark and melatonin can promote circadian adaptation in night shift workers' *Sleep Medicine Reviews* **6** (5) 407-420

Driskell J E 'The efficacy of naps as a fatigue countermeasure: A meta analytic integration' *Human Factors* 2005 **47** (2) 360-377

European Foundation for the Improvement of Living and Working Conditions *Continuous shift systems* 1998 Office for official publications of the European Communities, Bulletin of European studies on time No. 11/1998

Folkard S 'Is there a "best compromise" shift system?' *Ergonomics* 1992 **35** (12) 1453-1463

Folkard S and Akerstedt T 'Trends in the risk of accidents and injuries and their implications for models of fatigue and performance' *Aviation, Space and Environmental Medicine* 2004 **75** (3 Suppl) A161-167

Effective shift handover: A literature review OTO 96 003 HSE 1996 Available online at www.hse.gov.uk/research/otohtm/1996/index.htm

Shiftwork, Health and Safety: An overview of the scientific literature 1978-1990 CRR 31/1992 HSE 1992 Available online at www.hse.gov.uk/research/crr_htm/index.htm

International Labour Organization *Working time: Its impact on health and safety* Occupational Safety and Health Research Institute 2003 Available online at www.ilo.org/public/english/protection/condtrav/publ/wtwo-as-03.htm

Janis I *Victims of Groupthink: A Psychological Study of Foreign-Policy Decisions and Fiascoes* Houghton Mifflin 1972 ISBN 0 39514044 7

Johns M W 'A new method for measuring daytime sleepiness: the Epworth sleepiness scale' *Sleep* 1991 **14** (6) 540-545

Josten E J C, Ng-A-Tham J E and Thierry H 'The effects of extended workdays on fatigue, health, performance and satisfaction in nursing' *Journal of Advanced Nursing* **44** (6) 643-652

Kogi K 'Linking better shiftwork arrangements with safety and health management systems' *Revista de Saúde Pública* 2004 **38** (Suppl) 72-79

Knauth P 'Designing better shift systems' Applied Ergonomics 1996 **27** (1) 39-44

Mohren D C, Jansen, N W, Kant I J et al 'Prevalence of common infections among employees in different work schedules' *Journal of Occupational and Environmental Medicine* 2002 **44** (11) 1003-1011 *Plus Erratum in: Journal of Occupational and Environmental Medicine* **45** (1) 105

Monk T 'What can the chronobiologist do to help the shift worker?' *Journal of Biological Rhythms* 2000 **15** (2) 86-94

Monk T H, Folkard S and Wedderburn A I 'Maintaining safety and high performance on shiftwork' *Applied Ergonomics* 1996 **27** (1) 17-23

National Institute for Occupational Health and Safety *Overtime and extended work shifts: Recent findings on illness, injuries and health behaviours* NIOSH Publications Dissemination DHHS (NIOSH) 2004 Publication Number 2004-143 Available online at www.cdc.gov/niosh/docs/2004-143

Reid K and Dawson D 'Comparing performance on a simulated 12 hour shift rotation in young and older subjects' *Occupational and Environmental Medicine* 2001 **58** 58-62

Roehrs T and Roth T 'Sleep, sleepiness, sleep disorders and alcohol use and abuse' *Sleep Medicine Reviews* 2001 **5** (4), 287-297

Smith L, Folkard S, Tucker P et al 'Work shift duration: a review comparing 8 hour and 12 hour shift systems' *Occupational and Environmental Medicine* 1998 **55** 217-229

Stutts J C, Wilkins J W, Osberg J S et al 'Driver risk factors for sleep-related crashes' *Accident Analysis and Prevention* 2003 **35** 321-331

Takeyama H, Kubo T and Itani T 'The nighttime nap strategies for improving night shift work in workplace' *Industrial Health* 2005 **43**, 24-29

Tucker P 'The impact of rest breaks upon accident risk, fatigue and performance: a review' *Work and Stress* 2003 **17** (2) 123-137

Tucker P, Folkard S and MacDonald I 'Rest breaks and accident risk' *The Lancet* 2003 **361** 680

Tucker P, Smith L, MacDonald I et al 'The impact of early and late shift changeovers on sleep, health and well-being in 8- and 12-hour shift systems' *Journal of Occupational Health Psychology* 1998 **3** (3) 265-275

Tucker P, Smith L, MacDonald I et al, 'Distribution of rest days in 12 hour systems: impacts on health, well being and on shift alertness' *Occupational and Environmental Medicine* 1999 **56** 204-214

Tucker P, Smith L, MacDonald I et al 'Effects of direction of rotation in continuous and discontinuous 8 hour shift systems' *Occupational and Environmental Medicine* 2000 **57** 678-684

Wilson J L 'The impact of shift patterns on healthcare professionals' *Journal of Nursing Management* 2002 **10** 211-219

Wortley V and Grierson-Hill L 'Developing a successful self-rostering shift system' *Nursing Standard* 2003 **17** (42) 40-42

Further information

HSE priced and free publications are available by mail order from HSE Books, PO Box 1999, Sudbury, Suffolk CO10 2WA Tel: 01787 881165 Fax: 01787 313995 Website: www.hsebooks.co.uk (HSE priced publications are also available from bookshops and free leaflets can be downloaded from HSE's website: www.hse.gov.uk.)

For information about health and safety ring HSE's Infoline Tel: 0845 345 0055 Fax: 0845 408 9566
Textphone: 0845 408 9577 e-mail: hse.infoline@natbrit.com or write to HSE Information Services, Caerphilly Business Park, Caerphilly CF83 3GG.

The Stationery Office publications are available from The Stationery Office, PO Box 29, Norwich NR3 1GN
Tel: 0870 600 5522 Fax: 0870 600 5533 e-mail: customer.services@tso.co.uk Website: www.tso.co.uk
(They are also available from bookshops.)

Printed and published by the Health and Safety Executive C100 06/06